gloom4

GLOOM BY JAKE REBER

1111 PRESS

2024

JAKE REBER

VATICGLITCH.NET

11:11 Press

1111press.com

GLOOM 4
infrasensory

The text blinked in and out. Digital vision and textures still coming into being. How did Velvet contact me? It still didn't quite make sense. Am I still in the subfloor?

DEATH IS CLOSE

Why did Velvet break protocol? TRUST NO ONE. Could it actually be Velvet? VLTVG3033?

I feel my skin crawling. Anxiety bleeds through in pixels. My mouth falls into a frown, stretching down, blending the distinct zones and materials of my body.

SEE THE LINK. AGAIN THE UNCERTAINTY HUMS WITHIN. I IGNORE THE FAINT BUZZ>

I CLICK IT.

EXTRACT. THE LAYERS BEGIN TO PEEL AWAY.

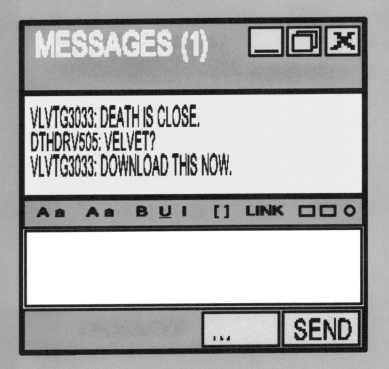

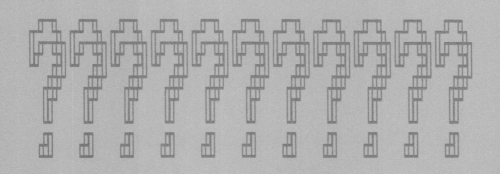

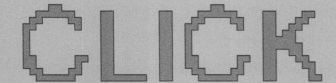

DOWNLOADING...

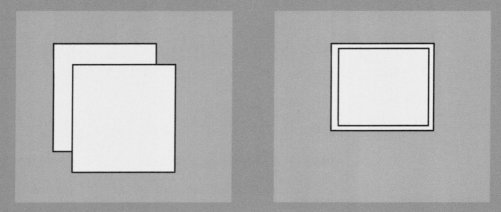

THE TASK IS NOW 5% COMPLETE. PLEASE WAIT...

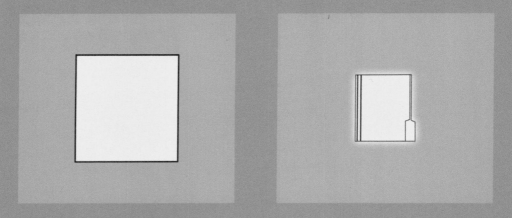

THE TASK IS NOW 13% COMPLETE. PLEASE WAIT...

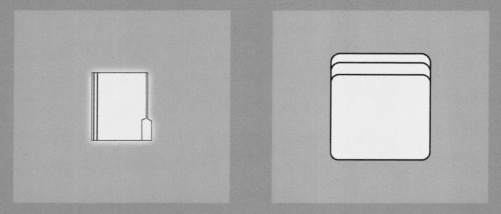

THE TASK IS NOW 35% COMPLETE. PLEASE WAIT...

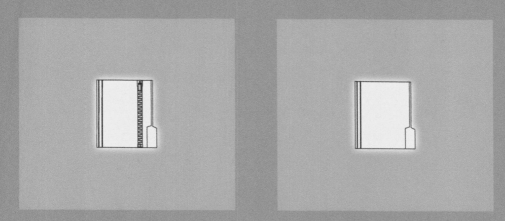

THE TASK IS NOW 77% COMPLETE. PLEASE WAIT...

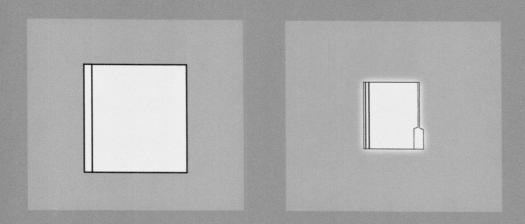

THE TASK IS NOW 93% COMPLETE. PLEASE WAIT...

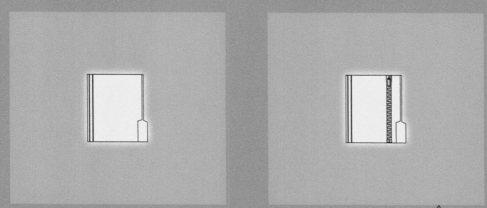

THE TASK IS NOW COMPLETE.

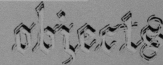

Walk into the cellar. Find the items that require your attention.

Do not fail. This is a condition of your existing in the realm. I repeat.

DO NOT FAIL.

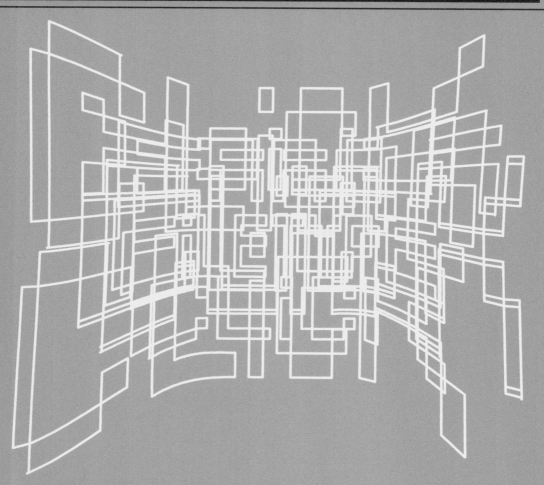

THE LINES AND LAYERS STARTED AS A
WIREFRAME, SLOWING FILLING IN COLOR AND
CONSISTENCY. THE WORLD BEGAN TO SOLIDIFY
AGAIN.

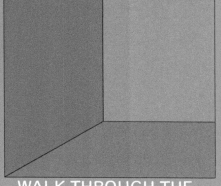

WALK THROUGH THE

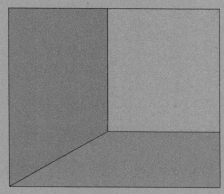

FIND THE STRANGE
CORNERS

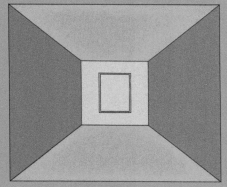

A DEAD END

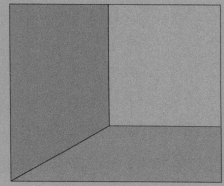

ANOTHER
CORNER

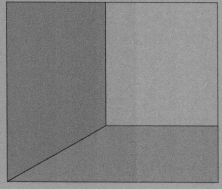

ANOTHER CORNER

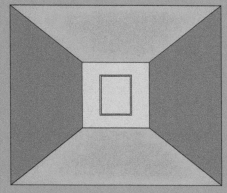

AND A DEAD END.

SOME MORE DULL HALLWAYS

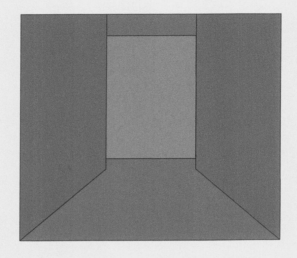

A FEW OBJECTS SCATTERED WITHIN

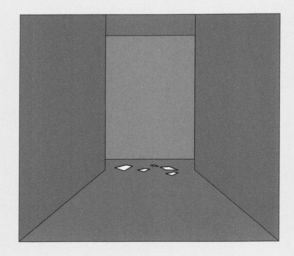

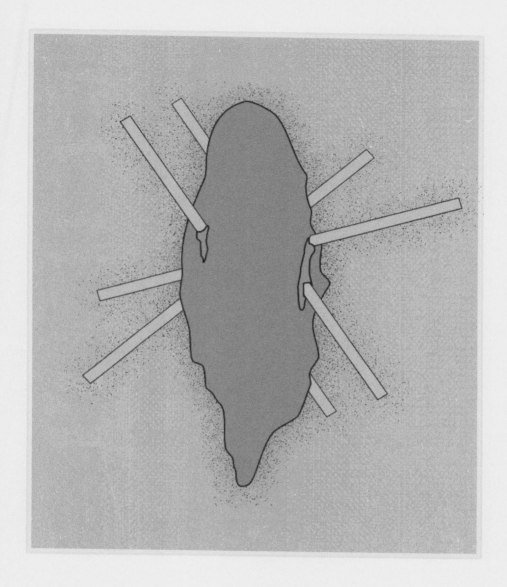

I REMEMBER ENCOUNTERING A STRANGE MEAT-LIKE FIGURE. THE FLESH HAD STEEL POSTS LOCKING IT IN PLACE> THE INSIDES RUNNING OUT. THEY HAD STARTED TO CONGEAL BY THE TIME I GOT THERE> IT LOOKED LIKE IT WAS NO LONGER IN PAIN< BUT IT WAS DEFINITELY SAD

THE PINK ROOM

The walls extend. Deeper and deeper. The .zip file still glowing. My arms reach towards the folder - trying to extract again. Another file another folder another extraction another another another.

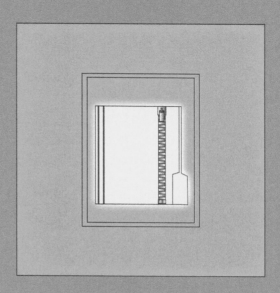

FINALLY> CONTACT MADE. PROCESS REPEAT> EXTRACT
FILE:

WAITING
WAAAIIIITTTTTINGGG

/   /   /   /   /   /

PROCESSING> PROCESSING> REQUEST GRANTED>

index

MY EYES DRIFT THROUGH THE STRANGE FILES> SOME APPEAR
TO BE FLOOR PLANS > OTHERS ARE CLEARLY DOCUMENTS
FROM OLD EXPERIMENTS > A FEW ON INFRASTRUCTURE.
GRANT APPLICATIONS. FUNDING STRUCTURES. PERSONNEL.
AND THEN SOME FILES THAT LOOK LIKE THEY WERE
RECOVERED FROM SOME TAMPERING. DIVING IN...

01:12:22	0293	1029389
03:17:48	1552	0312380
11:44:25	1093	0412801
06:32:42	1532	0128310
12:32:15	9931	0912393
06:33:42	0328	ERROR
02:47:11	2768	0383714
10:05:21	4382	ERROR
07:58:03	9201	ERROR
11:47:51	8356	ERROR
03:18:26	9214	ERROR
05:17:52	0515	ERROR

EMBODIMENT & CODED TACTILITY

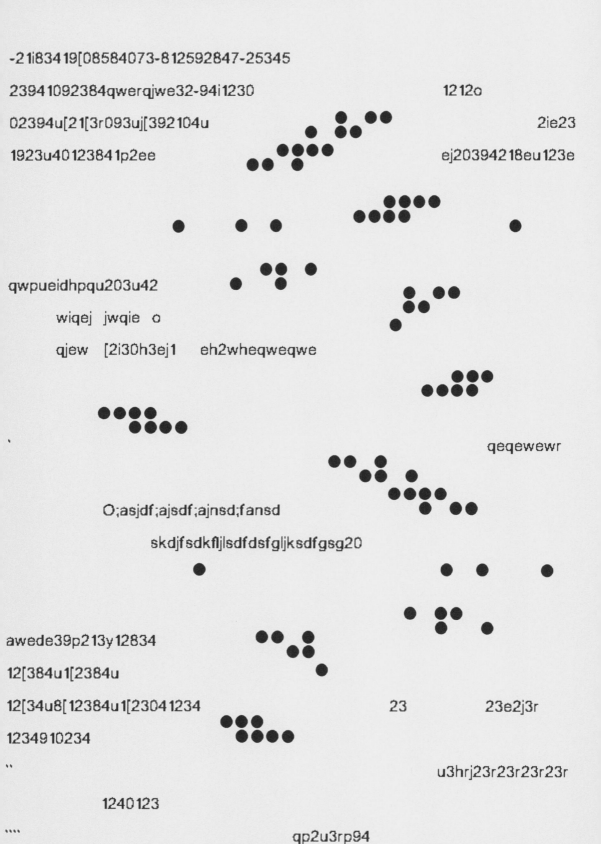

-21i83419[08584073-812592847-25345

23941092384qwerqjwe32-94i1230   1212o

02394u[21[3r093uj[392104u   2ie23

1923u40123841p2ee   ej20394218eu123e

qwpueidhpqu203u42

wiqej jwqie o

qjew [2i30h3ej1   eh2wheqweqwe

`

                                                        qeqewewr

O;asjdf;ajsdf;ajnsd;fansd

skdjfsdkfljlsdfdsfgljksdfgsg20

awede39p213y12834

12[384u1[2384u

12[34u8[12384u1[23041234   23   23e2j3r

1234910234

"

                                                        u3hrj23r23r23r23r

    1240123

""""   qp2u3rp94

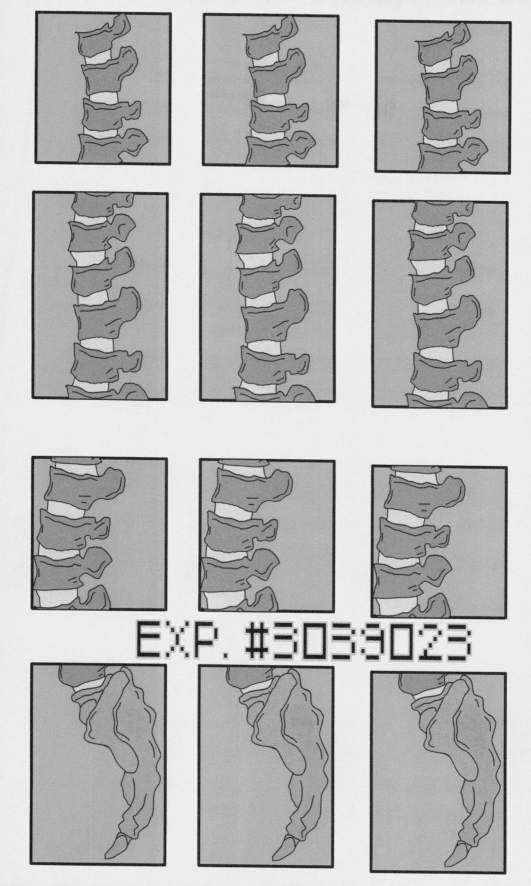

EXP. #3039023

SYMBOLIC FLOOR PLAN

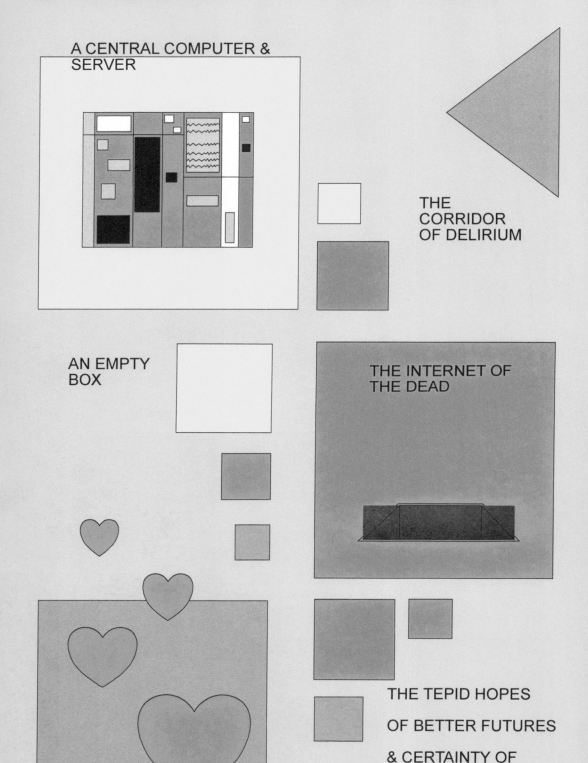

A CENTRAL COMPUTER & SERVER

THE CORRIDOR OF DELIRIUM

AN EMPTY BOX

THE INTERNET OF THE DEAD

THE TEPID HOPES

OF BETTER FUTURES

& CERTAINTY OF

FAILURE

ALGORITHMIC LUST & EROTICS

CLASSIFIED BIOTECH & EXPERIMENTAL PROCEDURES

THE LAYOUT & INFRASTRUCTURE

THE VARIOUS ROOMS ARE COLOR_CODED & ALL OTHER
INFORMATION HAS BEEN REDACTED. THE ROOMS SEEM
LIKE THEY ARE OVERLAPPING. POSSIBLY DIFFERENT FLOORS?
MAYBE DIFFERENT DESIGN PLANS? MULTIPLE VIRTUAL REALITIES?

THERE IS A BRIEF NOTE IN THE DOCUMENT:

1. REMOVE PROPRIETARY AND EXPERIMENTAL DOCS.
2. DESTROY OPTIC FIBER AND OTHER CONNECTIONS
3. SUBJECTS MUST BE PROCESSED AND RELOCATED
4. ONCE COMPLETE, REMOVE NOTE.

HUMAN TRIALS & CYBORG SPAWN SUBJECTS

ALL SUBJECTS FILED PAPERWORK AND
WAIVED LIABILITY. CLEAR TO PROCEED
THROUGH ENTIRE EXP. REGIMEN.
FINDINGS CATALOGUED IN GMIC.

APPLIED TESTS:

NDE_VISION_v3

COG_READ_v1.5

AIII PROCESSING_v5

REGEN_v2

```
1029371897301901298374
9812730487120398471029 8
3740192837409283741029 8
3740192873401287340192 8
7340198273409182734091 8
7304981273409817230498 7
1209384712093847109283 7
4109283741209837410928 3
7410928374120983741092 8
3741928347190238471293 7
```

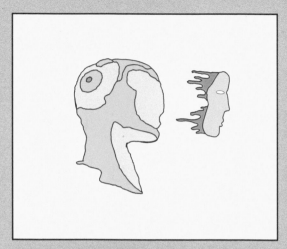

```
2138974012987340918273 4
0918273409172309418237 4
0192873401982374019283 7
4109238741092837401928 3
7410293874102938471209 3
8749012873410928374102 9
8347102983471092387419 2
0384710923847190283741 0
2983471029837412938471 2
9837412093487102938741 0
2938471029384710928347 3
```

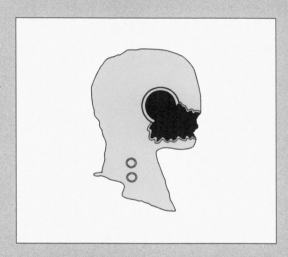

```
1209387698726348716239 8
7641872364817871632498 7
1236481723648917263491 8
7346918273641892734619 2
8734619287346129873461 9
8237461298734612983746 1
9283746192837461298734 6
1982374619287364981723 4
6291873461982734619827 3
4619823746192837416892 3
7419823641928374682173 4
```

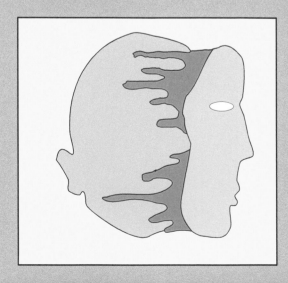

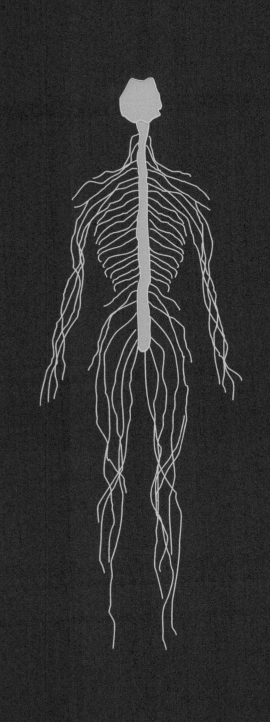

MICROSCAN 19283012

nterior mapping: -0832-1238-123-981-92-3

Depth_int: 1-2983-1923u-91283-12

Low0: 1-293-01923-1082-381-23-123-1023-12

Resistance: 109283019283-192-391283-1

Resp_liv: .05%

Hm_capacity: lv3 -238429834-232-4-23498

drkfrst: hrrhr0-23je2-je-3-23e-2j3je2j3-e-j23ej

Vidfeed: 1-023-981-283-9182-3918-2983-1823

Lngread: 12-038-1283-9182-381-238-1283

Notes:

These finding are preliminary, but they are quite promising. This subject is the first to display abilities and sensitivities beyond the threshold previously held as the scientific limit. Further tests are required to verify these findings.

SENSORY RESPONSIVENESS

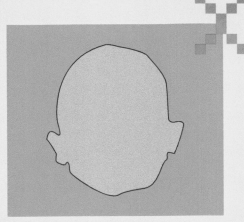

A SILICON HEAD

A PLANK

A MYSTERIOUS
DIAMOND

A CURSED MIRROR

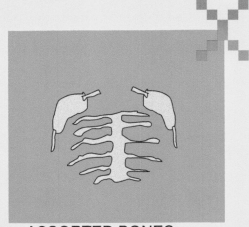

ASSORTED BONES

BROKEN GLASS

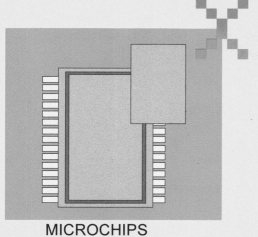

MICROCHIPS

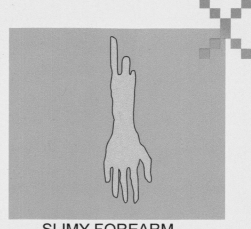

SLIMY FOREARM
FACIMILE

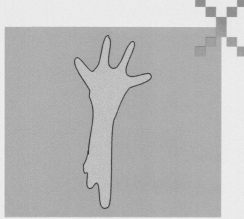

FAKE EXTRA-
TERRESTRIAL LIMB

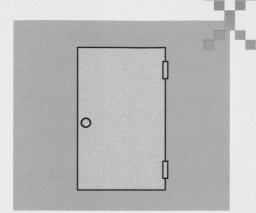

A STEEL DOOR

A POOL OF GOO

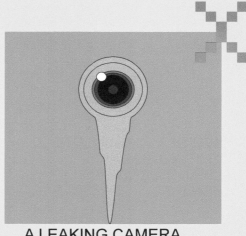

A LEAKING CAMERA

ADDITIONAL FILES & FOLDERS

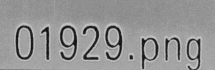

01929.png

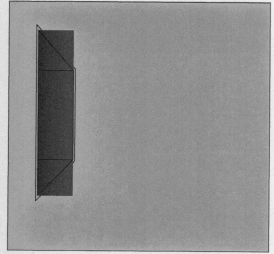

A BIOWASTE CUTOUT

1290009123.png

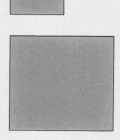

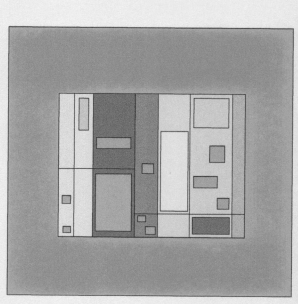

ANOTHER SET OF SERVERS
FOR CONTINUOUS
COMPUTATION AND
PROCESSING.

exp_091.png
exp_092.png
exp_093.png

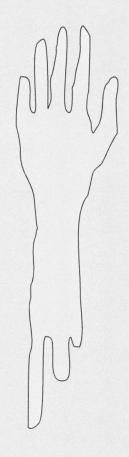

CORE DOCTRINE & PRACTICE

img01920ltrgy.png

ETERNAL PRAYERS FOR THOSE THAT MAKE CONTACT:

DO NOT TOUCH OR REPEAT THESE WORDS

DO NOT TOUCH OR REPEAT THESE WORDS

DO NOT TOUCH OR REPEAT THESE WORDS

"... the body splits and extends into all the realms, becoming one and many, within and without, an elemental shift towards the luminous and wonderous darkness, a simple act of attention, forever and ever and ever, a glitched sensation of material and immaterial, the infinite and the nothing..."

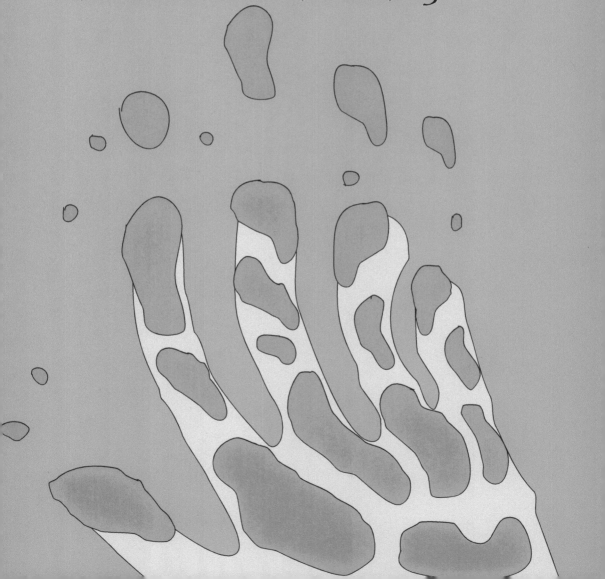

...beh...
...realms, bec...

with... and wi...

towards the l...

darkness, a s...

forever and e...

sensation of m...

the infinite and...

und extends into

ning one

out, an eleme

inous and wonderous

ple act of attention

A LIVING, BREATHING, TEXT

a glitched

rial and immaterial

thing..."

????

icon013.png

... maybe the text is within

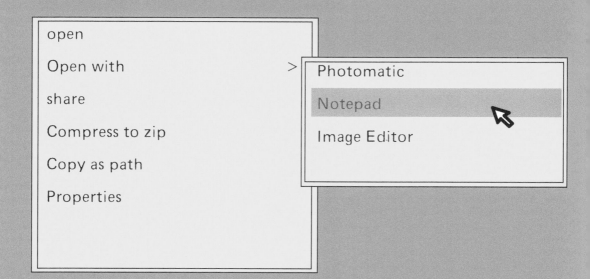

Milton Keynes UK
Ingram Content Group UK Ltd.
UKHW051016030624
443482UK00006B/34

9 798869 374868